Also available from Warner Books

CREATURE FEATURE VOLUME 2

CREATURE FEATURE
1

...BY DAVE FOLLOWS.

WARNER BOOKS

A *Warner* Book

First published in Great Britain
by Warner Books in 1994

Copyright © Dave Follows & Advance Features 1994

The moral right of the author has been asserted.

A CIP catalogue record for this book
is available from the British Library.

ISBN 0 7515 0775 X

Printed in England by Clays Ltd, St Ives plc

Warner Books
A Division of
Little, Brown and Company (UK) Limited
Brettenham House
Lancaster Place
London WC2E 7EN

TWANG!

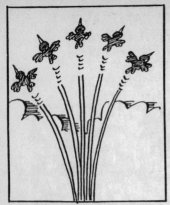

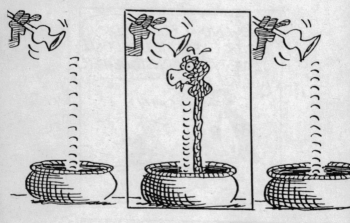

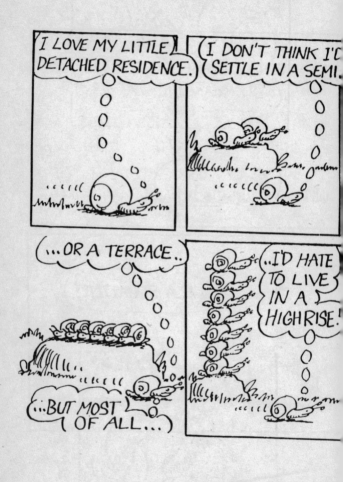

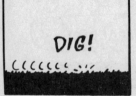

DIG!

DIG!

URRRGH!

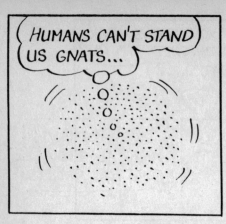

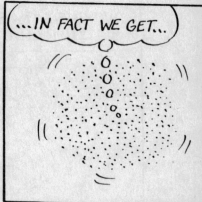

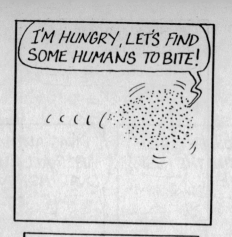

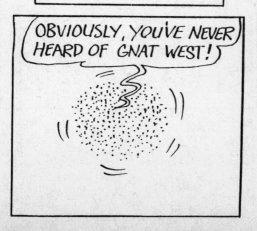

CREATURE FEATURE

appears in...

The FUNDAY TIMES

Evening Telegraph

The Journal

Evening News

HULL DAILY Mail

Lincolnshire Echo

Telegraph & Argus

Chronicle & Echo

Evening Advertiser

GLOUCESTERSHIRE Citizen

Eastern Daily Press

Evening News

Western Morning News